VARIATIONS.

Enigma.

Edward Elgar, Op. 36.

I.

(C. A. E.)

4

II.
(H. D. S-P.)

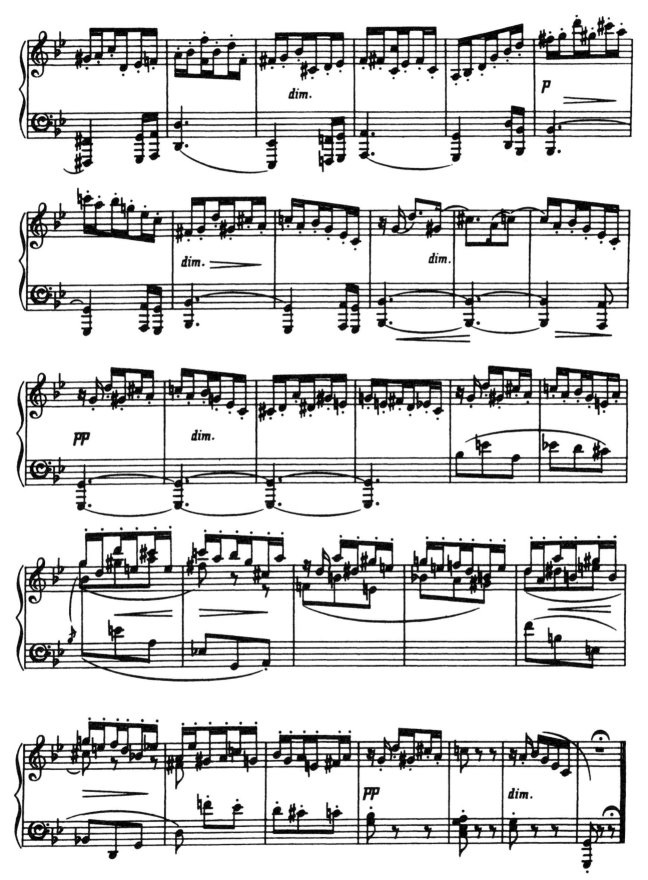

III.
(R. B. T.)

IV.

(W. M. B.)

V.

(R. P. A.)

attacca.

10815

VI.

(Ysobel.)

VII.
(Troyte.)

VIII.
(W. N.)

* The composer's recording is played at ♪ = 104, but the MS. and previous editions are marked ♩. = 52. It would appear that when altering the metronome from ♪ to ♩. the composer inadvertently divided by 2 instead of 3.

10813   Novello & Company, Ltd October 1949

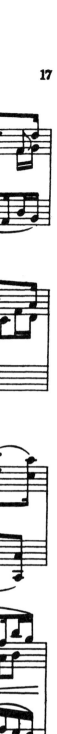

IX.

(Nimrod.)

X.

(Dorabella.)

Intermezzo.

XI.
(G. R. S.)

XII.
(B. G. N.)

* When this movement is played separately it may end with this chord.

XIII.

(✱ ✱ ✱)

XIV.
(E. D. U.)
Finale.

42

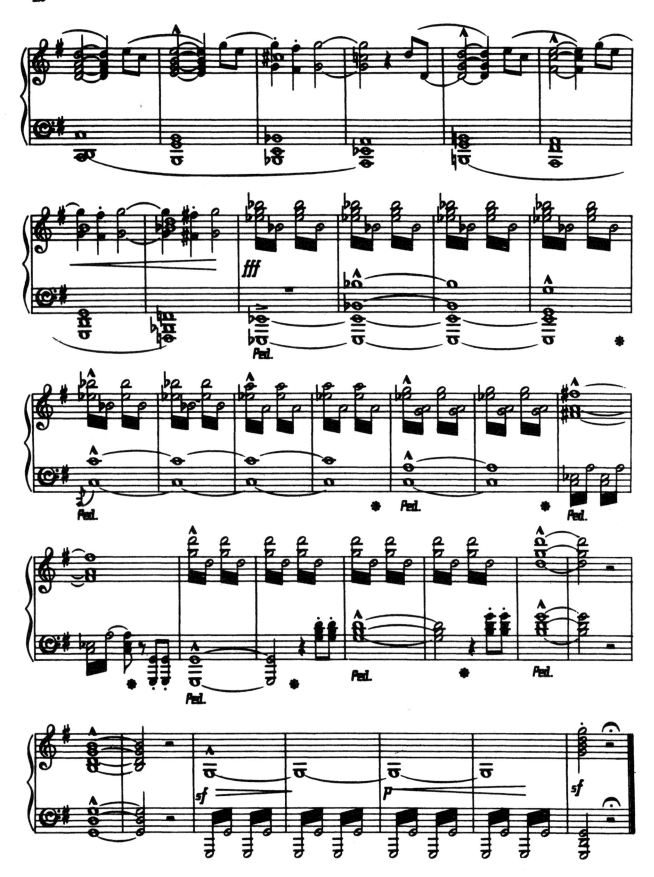

Caligraving Limited Thetford Norfolk